Published by West Cheshire Museums,
Grosvenor Museum, 27 Grosvenor Street,
Chester, Cheshire, CH1 2DD
www.westcheshiremuseums.co.uk

Designed by Rachid Taibi, The Upright One

ACKNOV

This g
the re:
of the ....
to a museum. The project was funded by
the Heritage Lottery Fund, Cheshire West
and Chester Council, Manage +, WREN, and
Historic England.

This book has been produced by Chris
Hewitson. Photographs have been produced
by Chris Hewitson, David Sejrup, Bernard
Rose, Edward Roberts, Tony Yoward and
using images contained in the Lion Salt
Works collection. The illustrations have
been produced by Chris Hewitson and
Cheryl Quinn.

PART OF
**WEST CHESHIRE
MUSEUMS**

Welcome

Stove House 5

At first glance Stove House 5 has stood since the last salt worker threw down his tools and left the gate ajar.

Yet, it is new, designed to mock and mimic the building that stood before. The entrance, through a fissure in the corner, reveals the once decrepit nature of the building. Inside, reused bricks and beams are the only trace of old amongst new. Gaze out through the window upon the pan that once bubbled with brine.

Where does salt come from?

Salt in Cheshire comes from beneath the ground. Cheshire has a distinct geology: A large, shallow basin formed between the sandstone ridge of the Delamere Forest to the west and the Cheshire Hills to the east.

In the Triassic Period c. 220 million years ago this was a large tropical lagoon that trapped seawater which evaporated leaving halite better known as rock salt (NaCl, Sodium Chloride).

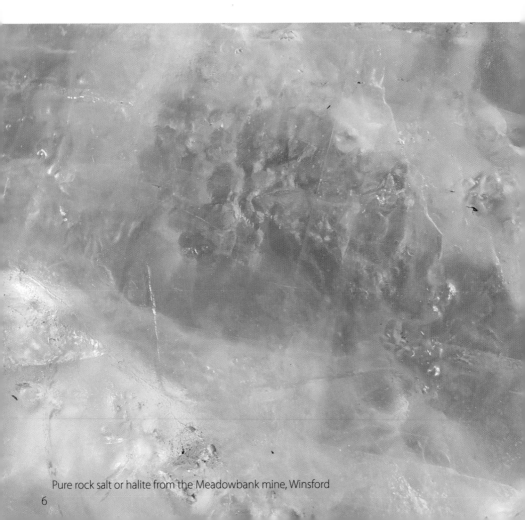

Pure rock salt or halite from the Meadowbank mine, Winsford

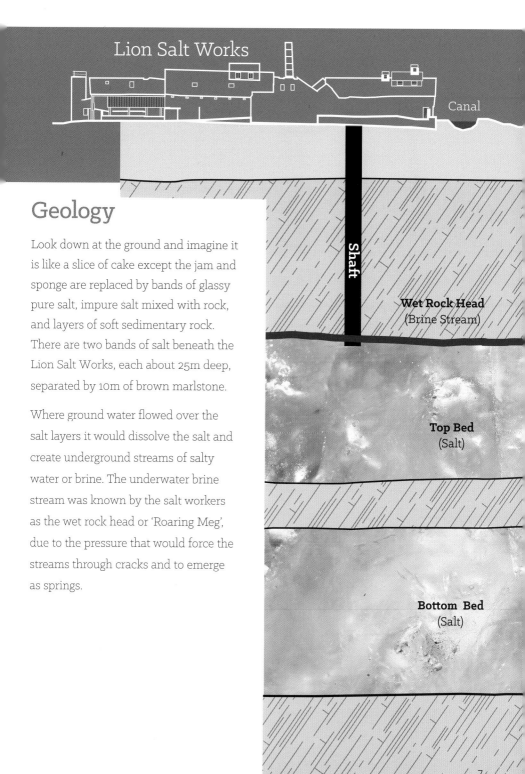

Lion Salt Works

Canal

Shaft

Wet Rock Head
(Brine Stream)

Top Bed
(Salt)

Bottom Bed
(Salt)

Geology

Look down at the ground and imagine it is like a slice of cake except the jam and sponge are replaced by bands of glassy pure salt, impure salt mixed with rock, and layers of soft sedimentary rock. There are two bands of salt beneath the Lion Salt Works, each about 25m deep, separated by 10m of brown marlstone.

Where ground water flowed over the salt layers it would dissolve the salt and create underground streams of salty water or brine. The underwater brine stream was known by the salt workers as the wet rock head or 'Roaring Meg', due to the pressure that would force the streams through cracks and to emerge as springs.

Brine Pumping

Salt is produced by two methods evaporating brine or mining. Brine has been evaporated since prehistoric man recognised that some springs had a salty taste. Rock salt mining began much later in the 1670s. By the 19th century, brine was extracted from the ground via a brine shaft or bore-hole and raised by means of pumps powered by steam engines.

Above: The pump on site was known as the 'Nodding Donkey', as when it was working the beam would go up and down like a donkey feeding. Brine would then be passed around the site in pipes.

Below: Brine was first stored in the brine tank and then subsequently delivered to the salt pans.

Pump and Boiler House

The Nodding Donkey was driven by the steam engine in the Pump House. Steam from a boiler created pressure to drive the pistons, turn the cogs and flywheel and move a shaft connected to the Nodding Donkey.

Top left: Cornish type boiler made by Abraham Lord of Rochdale located in the small shed next to the Manager's House.

Top right: Flywheel from the steam engine.

Bottom left: Governor from the steam engine designed to regulate the pistons.

Bottom right: Drive wheel and reduction gear from the steam engine.

The Galleries
The Red Lion

The Red Lion Inn was built to quench the thirst of the workers. Former cottages, where families of salt workers once lived were altered in 1899 to a simple public house. This replaced an earlier hotel on the site with the same name.

The displays take you through 2,000 years of salt-making, from the Romans, Saxons, and medieval times, up to the 19th century. Beyond the display recreates the Thompson's simple office, the bar of the Red Lion Inn and a waller's hut, where the workers would have their breakfast.

Thompson Family

The story of the salt works involved six generations of the same family. The Thompson family business dated back to 1842 and they owned salt mines, salt works, a boatyard and shipping business in Northwich and Winsford.

The first salt works on site was called the Alliance Works and was run by John (senior), and his sons John (Junior), Jabez and grandson Alfred Jabez Thompson. Another grandson Henry Ingram Thompson set up the Lion Salt Works in 1894 and ran it with his sons Jack and Alan Kinsey. After the Second World War Alan Kinsey's son, Henry Lloyd and Jack's grandson Jonathon followed the family tradition

Top left: Henry Ingram Thompson, set up the Lion Salt Works

Top right: Jack and Alan Kinsey Thompson at the Sandiway Golf Club.

Centre: The Thompson family on an outing on their Weaver Flat the Nautilus in 1888. Jabez and John (Junior) Thompson sit in the foreground on the step, Henry Ingram stands behind.

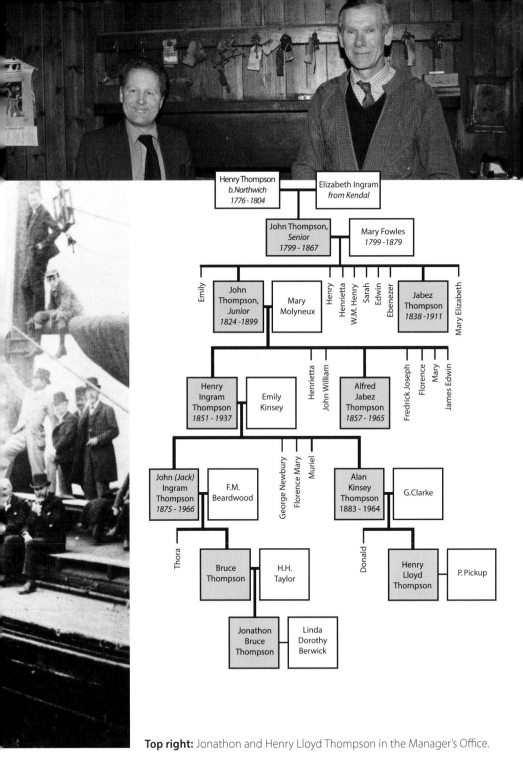

Henry Thompson
b.Northwich
1776 - 1804

Elizabeth Ingram
from Kendal

John Thompson,
Senior
1799 - 1867

Mary Fowles
1799 -1879

Emily

John
Thompson,
Junior
1824 -1899

Mary
Molyneux

Henry
Henrietta
W.M. Henry
Sarah
Edwin
Ebenezer

Jabez
Thompson
1838 -1911

Mary Elizabeth

Henry
Ingram
Thompson
1851 - 1937

Emily
Kinsey

Henrietta
John William

Alfred
Jabez
Thompson
1857 - 1965

Fredrick Joseph
Florence
Mary
James Edwin

John (*Jack*)
Ingram
Thompson
1875 - 1966

F.M.
Beardwood

George Newbury
Florence Mary
Muriel

Alan
Kinsey
Thompson
1883 - 1964

G.Clarke

Thora

Bruce
Thompson

H.H.
Taylor

Donald

Henry
Lloyd
Thompson

P. Pickup

Jonathon
Bruce
Thompson

Linda
Dorothy
Berwick

Top right: Jonathon and Henry Lloyd Thompson in the Manager's Office.

13

Salt Workers

The Thompson's ran the salt works, but the work was done by the local men and women of Marston village.

Work in the salt works was hard, physical and tiring. Most of the work involved raking, shovelling and heavy lifting. The workers were a mass of sinewy muscle. At its peak the Lion Salt Works employed 40-50 men and women. They had evocative names such as 'Lumpers', 'Lofters' and 'Wallers', but also included packers, smiths and joiners.

Salt was made in buildings called pan and stove houses. Here brine would be boiled in large iron pans to produce salt. The vapour rising from the boiling pan would cloud the entire room. The heat and humidity would force the men to strip off their shirts and work bare chested in simple shorts known as drawers and workman's clogs.

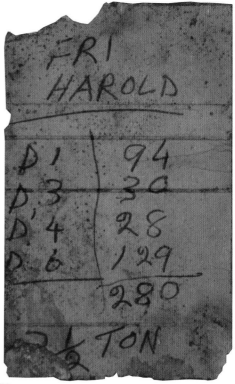

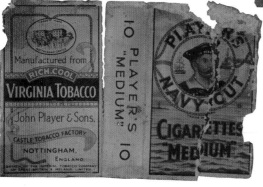

Above: The men worked on a piece basis for some tasks. They got paid for how many tons of salt they made. On the back of an old cigarette packet wedged in the corner of a door frame, salt workers had marked up how much salt they had made in a day: 280 lumps making up 3½ tons.

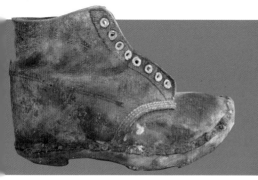

Salt was so corrosive to everything that the workers adopted heavy wooden clogs. This pair was discovered hidden under floor boards during the restoration of Stove House 2.

The wooden platforms around the pans would be slick with moisture. The work could be dangerous: one slip and you were in the boiling brine. Accidents were not common but men did die. In the 1930s, Gerald Lowe, aged 31, fell in the pan and was badly scalded. He rode his bicycle home where a doctor was called and he sadly died.

Above: A 'lumper' stands by the pan at the Lion Salt Works in about 1900. They raked, and skimmed the salt in the pan before putting it into tubs to make 'lumps' of salt. He is surrounded by salt lumps made in conical peg-top tubs. Stripped to the waist because of the heat, he has hung his shirt at the back of the pan house.

Above: The picture by former salt worker Tom Lightfoot shows a Waller's Hut, a tea room with a stove and a tea caddy sat on top boiling all day long. The Waller's were a breed apart. They were seen as less skilled than the other salt workers but they were certainly tough as they worked on the larger common pans, outside in the open air. They worked all day long no matter what the weather, making salt which they stored on the sides in huge piles or 'walls'.

15

The Red Lion Hotel and the Alliance Works

The buildings we see today are not the first on site. Originally near the road were some cottages and a hotel called the Red Lion. As the salt industry came to dominate the towns of Northwich, Winsford and Middlewich in the 19th century, the landscape was transformed from rural tranquillity into thriving industry.

The Red Lion was converted from a house in the 1820s. It served the salt workers and canal boatmen with beer and food. A coal yard and several squalid cottages were built to the north. The Lion Salt Works were built on the site when they were demolished.

To the east John Thompson (Senior) and his son John (Junior) bought a plot of land and started a salt works in 1856.

It was known as the Alliance Works. The salt works were run in the 1870s by John Junior's brother Jabez Thompson and in the 1880s by his son Alfred Jabez. He like many other manufacturers sold the business in 1888 to the Salt Union. The Salt Union was a powerful business monopoly that bought up salt works, closing older ones down. They shut the Alliance Works and demolished the buildings.

Above: Jabez Thompson expanded the salt works in the 1870s. He also ran a brickworks in Northwich. The brick bearing his mark was found during archaeological excavation.

Right: The workers would put salt in their beer to make up for all the sweat they had expended during the day. This bottle was found on site during excavations and is from local brewers N. P. Sandiford of Northwich.

Left: Under Stove House 5 the remains of buildings of the Alliance Works survived as brickwork walls. Originally a smithy it later became a cottage that was still lived in during the 1950s.

Trent and Mersey Canal

Red Lion Yard

Red Lion Hotel

ldw Lane

Smithy

Pans & Stove House

Shaft

Pans

Pans

8

Pans

Pans

10

Pans

Stove House

Rail & Shed

Pans

Pans

Pans

Pans

Pans

ALLIANCE SALT WORKS

Pans

Pans

Pans

Pans

Pans

Pans & Stove House

Basin

Brine Cistern

Above & bottom left: Excavations in 2014 showed that other buildings were located just below the surface of the ground

Archaeologists have used maps, plans and old documents to establish the size and extent of the Alliance Works. The remains of the salt works survive as brick walls beneath the play area and car park. This was one of many salt works that lined the canal in Marston and Wincham.

The Lion Salt Works

Salt was in the Thompson's blood and it was not long before they had set up a new business. In 1894 Henry Ingram Thompson bought the site of the Red Lion Hotel. He set up the Lion Salt Works right next door to the old one.

Top: In 1965, Pan and Stove House 5 were the last to be built on site. The pan house collapsed in 1995 and the stove house has been rebuilt as the visitor's centre.

Centre: The Engine House and Brine Tank (right) was built in 1894. Adjacent is the headstock that would have covered the brine shaft. Stove House 2 (left) was built in 1899 after a number of cottages were demolished.

Bottom: Pan and Stove House 1 were built in 1894 (left). The photo dates to around 1920. Little survives of the original buildings but the site is visible as the garden by the bridge. The Coronation Salt Store (right) originally had an arched roof.

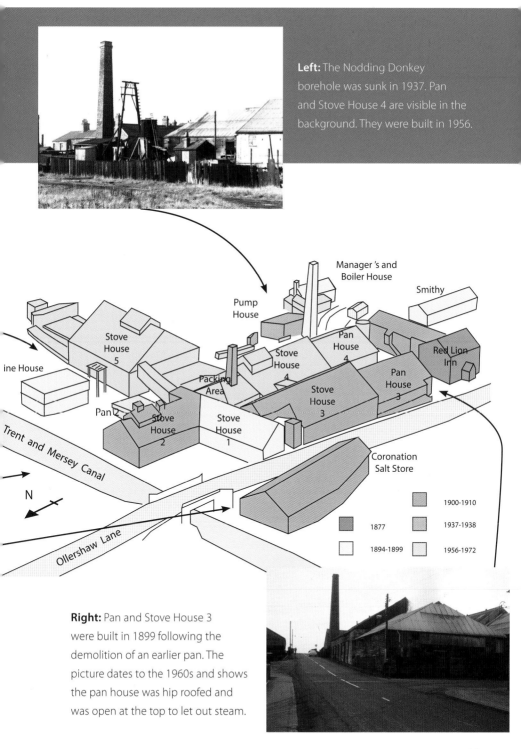

Left: The Nodding Donkey borehole was sunk in 1937. Pan and Stove House 4 are visible in the background. They were built in 1956.

Manager's and Boiler House

Smithy

Pump House

Pan House 4

Red Lion Inn

Stove House 5

Stove House 4

Pan House 3

ine House

Packing Area

Stove House 3

Pan 2

Stove House 2

Stove House 1

Trent and Mersey Canal

N

Coronation Salt Store

Ollershaw Lane

	1900-1910
1877	1937-1938
1894-1899	1956-1972

Right: Pan and Stove House 3 were built in 1899 following the demolition of an earlier pan. The picture dates to the 1960s and shows the pan house was hip roofed and was open at the top to let out steam.

19

The Restoration Story

By the 1960s open-pan salt making was in decline. Modern production of vacuum evaporated salt dominated the market. Other traditional salt makers such as Seddons and Murgatroyds closed but the Lion Salt Works soldiered on.

The majority of their salt continued to be exported to West Africa. In Nigeria, the Biafran War of the 1960s and the military juntas that followed disrupted this market and by 1986 they were forced to close.

The idea of a museum had begun in the early 1980s when Henry Lloyd and Jonathon Thompson had successfully opened the salt works to the public. On closure the local council purchased the site and the Lion Salt Works Trust was formed. The trust ran the museum and operated as fundraisers as the restoration began.

These were old industrial buildings, designed for work and not to last. Salt leached into the joints, decayed the brickwork; metal rusted and buckled. Where holes formed in the roof rain poured in and wood rotted. Radical restoration plans were formulated supported by a generous grant from the Heritage Lottery Fund. The restoration was completed in 2015 and opened to the public as a museum and visitor's attraction.

The Boiling Pan
Pan House 3

Pan House 3 has been designed to give the visitor the impression of the steam laden pan house.

As the brine came to the boil, steam would rise in clouds filling the void and escape through the ceiling. Heat would radiate from the brick of the kiln and the iron of the pan. The men would be stripped to the waist hard at work. The taste of salt would cling to the edges of their lips and fill their nostrils.

In the centre of the pan house was a large brick kiln containing four furnaces. Coal and later oil fires in the furnaces heated the brine-filled, iron pan above.

The salt workers stood on either side of the pan on wooden walkways known as 'hurdles'.

The Pan: 'Making the brine chuckle'

Natural brine was boiled in a pan to evaporate water. When the salt began to boil it was said to 'chuckle' as crystals of salt would form and drop to the bottom of the pan.

Salt-making was a 'dark art' and the salt workers would add all sorts of things to make the salt crystals form. This included strong ale, bullock's blood and eggs, but these were replaced by soft soap and glue. The crystals were raked-up, skimmed and lumped to make salt.

The coarsest grade of salt known as common salt was boiled outside in large 'common' or 'fishery' pans. Finer varieties were made in smaller 'fine' pans in covered wooden buildings called pan houses. The salt was made into lumps that were dried and crushed in an adjacent brick building called the stove house. A salt pan like the one in Pan House 3, produced around about 35 to 40 tons of salt weekly.

Above: Pan House 3, photographed in 1966. Coal was used to fire the kiln. Automated hoppers had replaced manual shovelling and this was later replaced by oil.

1. Firing: The brick kilns beneath the pan were fired with coal. A slow fire was required to provide a steady heat, and it was a skilled job undertaken by the fireman.

2. Raking-Up: The salt was drawn to the sides of the pan using large heavy rakes, and formed heaps.

3. Skimming: The salt was removed using ladles called 'skimmers' that allowed excess brine to drain out. The best salt was put in rectangular tubs.

4. Lumping: The salt put in tubs was made into 'lumps'. They would then be 'turned out' in a row. For this reason the salt workers in the pan house were known as 'lumpmen'.

5. Barrowing: The lumps of salt formed in the pan were barrowed into the hothouse.

6. Drying: The lumps were placed in rows on the flues to dry. The lumps would take two weeks to dry. The 'lofter' was the salt worker who worked in the hothouse.

7. Lofting: The warehouse floor contained a series of hatches that were opened in turn. The lofters passed-up the dry salt lumps to the warehouse.

8. Packing: The lumps were crushed, bagged and packaged for market in the warehouse.

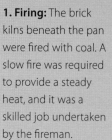
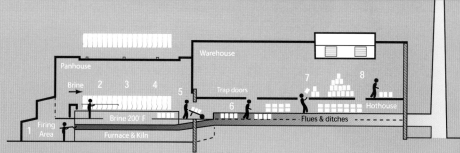

PAN HOUSE   STOVE HOUSE

Tools of the trade

There were many distinctive tools associated with making salt. Each had a specific function.

Rake: The large rakes used to scrape the salt to the side of the pan had iron heads. They were flung out into the pan and drawn back hand-over-hand.

Skimmer: The skimmer was used to take the salt out of the pan. It had a scooped shape with holes like a colander to drain the excess brine.

Mundling Stick: This odd-shaped wooden bat was used to compress the salt in the tubs when they were making 'heavy shoots', in other words dense compressed lumps, typically for Dairy salt.

Lofting prong: If the lumps were due to be crushed the lofters would use a prong to spike the lumps and throw them up to the warehouse through the salt hatches.

Tubs: Lump salt was originally made in wicker baskets and was referred to as bushels. By the 19th century they were using square plan tubs made of elm wood, nailed together with brass tacks. These were replaced by fibreglass tubs from the 1960s

Happer: If the salt was sold to market as 'block salt' it was finished off with a table tennis shaped paddle.

Drying and Packing
The Stove House

Making the salt was the first stage. It then had to be dried and packed ready for market. This was undertaken in the stove houses: the large brick buildings behind the pan houses. On the lower floor was the 'hothouse', on the upper floor was a warehouse.

The Hothouse

The hothouse or 'hotties' was covered in low brick tunnels called flues with iron plates on top. The heat from the hot air in the kiln passed through the flues and was recycled to dry the lumps of salt. The environment within the hothouse was an unpleasant mix of humid air and sulphurous waste gases from the burning coal.

Above: The lumps of salt would be placed on the flues and in the ditches completely filling the hothouse. The lumps would take two weeks to dry before they would be lofted to the warehouse above.

Opposite left: Stove House 5, with Stove House 2 in the background prior to restoration in 2004.

Right: The lumps of salt formed in the pan house were brought into the stove on barrows and placed on the flues to dry.

The Warehouse

The upper part of the stove house was a warehouse for storage and processing also known as the 'lump room' or 'mill room' in which the lumps would be stored and crushed in the mill.

In the 19th century women and children worked in the salt works undertaking tasks like crushing and packing salt and stitching bags in the warehouse. The heat from the pans and stoves meant that women worked scandalously in only their petticoats. By the 20th century children were barred from working in industry but women were found working in the warehouse.

Left: Many of the ladies were spouses of the men who worked in the pan houses. Here they are packing crushed salt into small plastic packets.

Right: Henry Lloyd Thompson loads salt into the hopper of the crushing mill in the warehouse in Stove House 4.

The crushing mill in Stove House 4 was originally located in the warehouse of Stove House 2 at the north of the site. It was powered by a steam engine but converted to electricity in the 1950s. Salt lumps were put in the hopper. Inside the mill were cutting knives and rollers that crushed the salt lumps. Sieves graded them into different sizes of salt and they were bagged at the bottom.

Salt Types

Different types of salt could be made by adding different agents and boiling salt at different temperatures. Fishery and common salt was mad in pans outside at temperatures between 38°C (100°F) and 76°C (170°F). Salt approaching boiling point (100°C, 212°F) was made in the pan house.

Dairy Salt: This was a heavy salt with very little volume (80lb/cubic foot), lumps produced in a fine pan with soft-soap additive and then crushed and sieved.

Common Salt: This was a mass produced salt that took one, two or three days to produce at temperatures of 160-170°F (70-76°C) and comprised the industrial chemical grades, which were separated into coarse, medium or fine common.

Fishery Salt: The coarsest grade of salt took 7 days, 14 days or longer to produce and was known as 'fishery salt'. A temperature of 38°C (100°F) produced a coarse, hard, slow-melting crystal salt that was used to pack fish when it was caught at sea or to preserve fish when the catch was returned to dock.

Bay Salt: When fishe salt was sieved for the largest crystals it was known as 'bay salt' after French sola evaporated sea salt that had a similar coarseness.

Factory Filled and Lagos salt was light, high volume salt (53 lb/ cubic foot). It was also made into lumps and crushed. It was 'run of the mill' salt and the size was due to being passed through the crushing mill. Shipping merchants supplied 40 pound cloth bags and it was sold to West Africa.

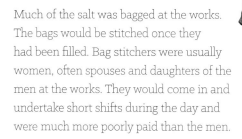

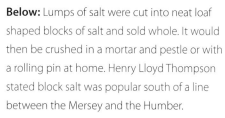

Much of the salt was bagged at the works. The bags would be stitched once they had been filled. Bag stitchers were usually women, often spouses and daughters of the men at the works. They would come in and undertake short shifts during the day and were much more poorly paid than the men.

Below: Lumps of salt were cut into neat loaf shaped blocks of salt and sold whole. It would then be crushed in a mortar and pestle or with a rolling pin at home. Henry Lloyd Thompson stated block salt was popular south of a line between the Mersey and the Humber.

Above and below: The bags would be marked with stamps or stencils showing the destination or type of salt.

The Salt Story
Stove House 3 and 4

The displays in Stove House 3, tell how salt was made. In the display boxes along one wall mannequins show the different acts of salt-making. In the centre of the room interactive displays reveal how the water cycle and salt production interact.

The displays in Stove House 4 explore the science of salt-making. The crushing mill dominates the centre of the room. Listen to former salt workers tell their stories in their own voices.

35

The Manager's House

Generation after generation, the Thompson's ran the salt works from the manager's house. They would sit in the warmth of the office on cold winter mornings, taking orders for salt to be exported around the world to Europe, Canada or West Africa.

Above: The Manager's House: the timber-frame was designed to protect against subsidence.

Left: The workers would come in at the end of the week, and their wages would be divvied-out in sardine tins. The hatch was used to hand out wages, or deliver orders.

Above: Henry Lloyd Thompson enjoys the heat of the range in the Manager's House

Left: Orders were taken from their shipping office in Liverpool at Rumsford Street and 'Saltcastle'. Telegrams like these show that orders were sent to the domestic market in Manchester or down the River Weaver to the docks at Weston Point or Liverpool for export. Key markets included salt to Denmark for curing bacon and ham, to the fisheries industry in Canada and Lagos salt to West Africa.

The Smithy

The salt works were not designed to last. There was a constant battle against the corrosive effect of salt, water and hot gases. The salt works employed smiths and carpenters to repair the salt buildings. The low, timber building by the entrance to the site housed the smithy and carpenter's workshops.

Above: Inside the first room was a forge, with an anvil and the smith's tools next to it.

Top right: Lighting within the pan and stove houses was poor. The walls were lime washed to reflect as much light as possible.

Bottom left: A collection of receipts from the salt works was recovered from the attic of the Red Lion Inn. Northwich had a network of suppliers providing iron plates for the pans, wood for the buildings, pipework, spare parts for the boilers and repairing the tools.

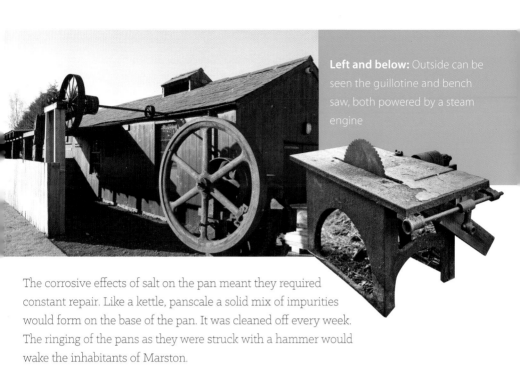

Left and below: Outside can be seen the guillotine and bench saw, both powered by a steam engine

The corrosive effects of salt on the pan meant they required constant repair. Like a kettle, panscale a solid mix of impurities would form on the base of the pan. It was cleaned off every week. The ringing of the pans as they were struck with a hammer would wake the inhabitants of Marston.

Below: Look at the pan outside Stove House 5. Why were the pans made of iron? The answer is that lead was too soft, stainless steel too expensive and iron was cheap and easy to repair. The pan is a patchwork of small panels that could be removed when they corroded and a new one riveted on.

The Salt Landscape
Stove House 2

Stove House 2 draws you into the distinctive local environment. The gallery looks at the environment and the plant and animal species that inhabit it.

The legacy of the salt industry is an altered landscape. The scenery today of silver birch woods and grass land is very different from when it was a forest of chimneys emitting smoke and shack-like industrial buildings, from which clouds of steam driven off from the brine, would shroud the roads and canal. The pollution damaged the surrounding land and it was described as a 'waste howling wilderness'.

Destructive changes were caused by salt mining and brine pumping. These left the flashes, lakes formed as depressions caused by subsidence filled with water. Industry deposited waste in these flashes to raise the ground and this altered the ecosystem. A new environment was created, part natural and part managed. Today a patch-work of eco-systems exist: lime-rich grasslands; flashes, streams and rivers fringed by reed beds; pockets of deciduous woodland and arable pastureland.

41

Canal and River

The Alliance and Lion Salt Works relied on narrow boats for deliveries of coal and shipping salt. Salt was taken along the canal to Anderton and transferred onto bigger boats on the River Weaver. At ports at Weston Point, Birkenhead and Liverpool it was put on ships to Canada and West Africa.

Left: Loading salt into a Thompson's narrow boat for transport to Anderton.

Right: Beside the Anderton Boat Lift was a series of salt chutes on jetties. Salt was unloaded from narrow boats into barrows and tipped down the chutes into the hold of the waiting Weaver Flat 'Constance'. Captain, Ernie Williamson and Sam Riddings lean against the rail.

Above: The Anderton Boat Lift was completed in 1875 allowing boats to pass from the Trent and Mersey Canal to the River Weaver.

Rail and Road

The Northwich rail lines were built in 1867 and a track ran into the centre of the Alliance Works. A new rail line was built in 1905 to serve the Lion Salt Works. By the 1950s, the canal, river and railway had fallen out of use. Lorries took the salt to the ports in Liverpool.

Above: The salt wagon sits on the rails at the site entrance. It is one of the last in the country. The pitched roof of the salt wagon was designed to keep the salt dry on the way to market

Left: The Thompson's built a loading bay so sacks could be taken from the warehouses and put directly in the back of the lorries. This example is from Murgatroyd's Work in Middlewich.

Below: The rail lines were exposed during restoration work. They arrived right in front of Pan House 3 and 4 and coal would be taken straight off and into the furnaces.

Left: The coal wagons would be open as they were not needed to be kept dry.

45

Subsidence in Northwich

The landscape of Northwich was profoundly shaped by the salt industry. Both mining, brine extraction and the resultant subsidence, created an environment of flashes and pools in a broad swathe between Northwich, Marston and Anderton.

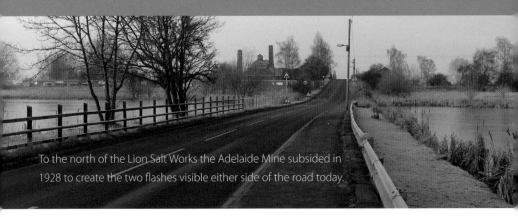

To the north of the Lion Salt Works the Adelaide Mine subsided in 1928 to create the two flashes visible either side of the road today.

The landscape of flashes prevented future development on the land and Northwich is blessed by having a natural environment that encroaches into the midst of the town centre.

After salt beds were discovered in the 1670s mines were dug in the top bed of salt and peppered the landscape. As water infiltrated the mines they collapsed with catastrophic consequences, sucking buildings down into a great funnel shaped hole.

From the 1780s most mines were dug into the bottom bed of salt. The area between Northwich and Marston became a network of inter-connected mines held up by pillars of salt. When the mines were abandoned they became underground reservoirs of brine as water dissolved the pillars. The roofs of the mines collapsed and from the 1840s to the 1920s three huge flashes of Witton, Ashton and Neumann formed. To the north of the Lion Salt Works the Adelaide Mine subsided in 1928 to create the two flashes visible either side of the road today.

Above: Subsidence could be dramatic. In 1907 the Trent and Mersey Canal breached where it passed over the Marston Hall Mine. See Walk 1.

In the town of Northwich the buildings are a mix of old and new but the casual eye would be forgiven for mistaking the black and white timber buildings of the high street as a result of the Tudor past. Instead traditional building techniques were revived. The timber-frames meant the buildings were stable when the ground subsided. They were then jacked-up above the water level. During the 1920s most of the high street was raised during the 'big lift'.

Top: The Warrington Road began to subside into the flashes. See Walk 2.

Bottom: The Witton Brook now runs in a narrow course. The land either side has been reclaimed. See Walk 2.

47

Walk 1

Transport along the Trent and Mersey Canal

Practicalities: The walk follows the towpath of the canal. The towpath can be muddy in winter and areas have subsided into the canal. It is therefore not suitable for children's buggies or wheelchairs. Small children should be accompanied when by the canal.

Distance and Time: The walk is 2 miles in length and should take 50 minutes to 1 hour at a steady pace.

This walk traces the route of salt as it left the Lion Salt Works on its journey to the docks at Weston Point, Liverpool and Birkenhead and from there to Europe, Canada and West Africa. It also reveals a landscape in which the ghosts of salt works shadow the canal.

Instead of heading to the main entrance, pass to the canal through the gate in the fence beyond the Children's Play Area. Turn left along the canal. Few instructions are needed from here as the walk follows the canal towpath for the next 2 miles.

A1. On the opposite bank of the canal are the remains of the Ollershaw Lane and Adelaide Flash. This mine collapsed in 1929 creating the flashes that can be seen today. The lumps and bumps in the fields are the remains of the old salt works. The remains of the Coronation Salt Store are on the left hand side. Salt from the Lion Salt Works was stored here before being transferred to canal boats and transported down the canal to Anderton. Further along on the left was the location of the Crystal Mine. All that remains is the Crystal Cottage now a private residence.

A2. The canal turns to the north-east and becomes very straight. This is where a bypass was built to take the canal around the subsiding remains of the Marston Old Mine, the earliest mine in Northwich. A dip in the towpath denotes where the mine is collapsing and some remains exist in the bushes.

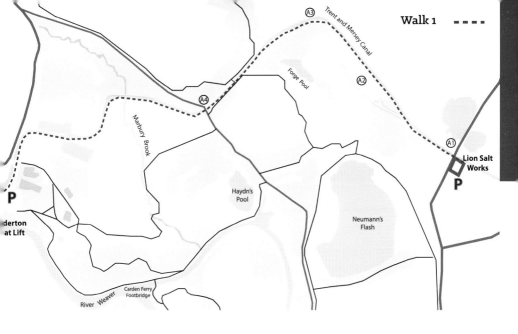

A3. The canal takes a sharp turn after about ½ a mile. It is transported on a high embankment. This is where the Marston Hall Mine has been continually subsiding. Almost six metres below the towpath in private woodland are the collapsed remains of the old mine and salt works. The canal collapsed here in 1907.

A4. A footbridge and the Marbury Lane Bridge give access to Marbury Park, the former residence of the Marbury family. Rock salt deposits were first discovered in the 1670s in woodland south of the canal.

The Anderton Boat Lift would allow boats to transfer from the canal to the River Weaver below. Boats would pass down the boat lift and tether alongside larger Weaver Flats and transfer their loads of salt. Before this the salt was sent down long chutes that lined the embankment on the right hand side of the boat lift.

Walk 2

The Northwich Woodlands

Practicalities: The walk follows pavements on the side of the road and good paved or gravel footpaths. The walk is suitable for bicycles or children's buggies. There is one difficult road crossing at the bottom of Wincham and children should be accompanied at all times. This walk can be combined with Walk 1 in reverse to make a round walk returning to the Lion Salt Works.

Distance and Time: The walk is about 2.2 miles in length and should take about 55 minutes to 1 hour 5 mins.

This walk passes through the landscape of the Northwich Woodlands. The area bears little resemblance to that which existed only sixty or seventy years ago. The land was riddled with subsidence and large flashes, lakes caused by collapsing mines. It is now pleasant woodlands and reed lined streams, the product of over 40 years of land reclamation.

B1. Out of the main entrance turn right onto Ollershaw Lane and follow the road. The entrance to the Northwich Woodlands is straight ahead and another crossing is at the turn to Wincham Lane. Take great care crossing the road.

B2. Through the gate, the path forks into three, continue straight ahead. This is the line of the Old Warrington Road and forms a causeway between the flashes of Ashton (to the left) and Neumann (to the right; see c1). Paths allow you to walk all the way around Neumann's and Ashton's Flashes, taking in the views and visiting the bird hides. At Marbury Lane turn right and walk up the lane. After ½ mile turn left onto a gravel path.

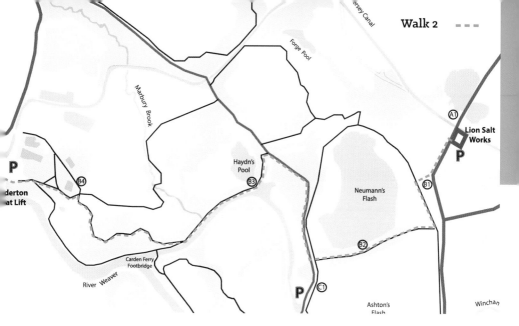

Lion Salt
Works

Forge Pool

Marbury Brook

Haydn's
Pool

Neumann's
Flash

...derton
...at Lift

Carden Ferry
Footbridge

River Weaver

Ashton's
Flash

Winchan

B3 Follow the path along the level adjacent to the Witton Brook. The Witton Brook was formally a large flash but much of the land you see has been reclaimed. At the junction bear left. Right takes you to Haydn's Pool and more bird hides. After ¼ mile the path forks, bear right up the slope up the hill and then left at the junction after 100 yards. The path brings you out into silver birch woodland. Cross over the brine pipelines on a wooden bridge.

B4. The path eventually brings you out in a clearing. The area is now known as Anderton Park. Turning left are views of the Winnington Works, a modern chemical works that sits on the location of Brunner Mond's original salt and chemical works founded in the 19th century. The path splits into cross-roads. If you continue straight ahead you will find two pools which were brine cisterns and are the last remains of the British Salt Works.

For the boat lift follow the path left. Bear left across the large clearing and the path leads to a car park and the Anderton Boat Lift is on the far side.

Walk 3

Northwich a town on the edge

Practicalities: The walk follows pavements on the side of the road and good paved or gravel footpaths. The walk is suitable for bicycles or children's buggies. There are a number of road crossings and children should be accompanied at all times.

Distance and Time: The walk is 2.2 miles long and should take 55 minutes to 1 hour 5 mins.

This walk takes you through the southern part of the Northwich Woodlands, taking in a landscape altered by subsiding mines. It then changes to take in the Northwich Town with its distinctive black and white houses, built to combat subsidence. The final part follows the line of the River Dane, where medieval salt workers once thrived.

C1. Follow instructions B1 and B2 for Walk 2. Follow the line of the Old Warrington Road between the flashes of Ashton (to the left) and Neumann (to the right). At the end of the path continue straight through the gate and turn left down the paved Marbury Lane. Alternatively turn left before the gate on the path for views of Ashton Flash. A board explains how the flashes were formed. Cross the Witton Brook on the black and white bridge and take the path marked Carey Park on the right hand side. Follow the signs through Carey Park to the entrance north of the town centre.

C2. Cross over the road and follow it right, before taking an immediate left through car parks down the road beside the Salvation Army. Crossing a small lane follow the ginnel onto the High Street. Webb and Sons Butchers are straight ahead.

The area is now the Baron's Quay Shopping Centre. Beneath the car parks were the remains of the Baron's Quay and Witton mines. They were filled in at a cost of £32 million pounds stabilising the northern part of the town centre.

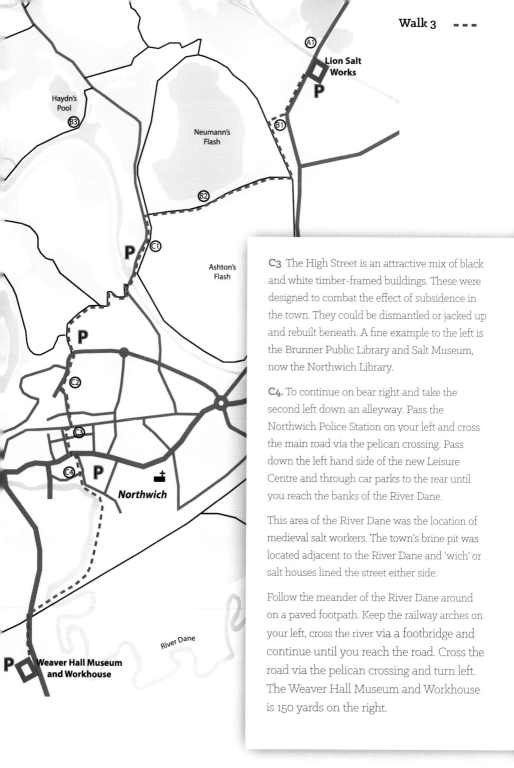

Lion Salt
Works

Haydn's
Pool

Neumann's
Flash

Ashton's
Flash

Northwich

River Dane

Weaver Hall Museum
and Workhouse

C3. The High Street is an attractive mix of black and white timber-framed buildings. These were designed to combat the effect of subsidence in the town. They could be dismantled or jacked up and rebuilt beneath. A fine example to the left is the Brunner Public Library and Salt Museum, now the Northwich Library.

C4. To continue on bear right and take the second left down an alleyway. Pass the Northwich Police Station on your left and cross the main road via the pelican crossing. Pass down the left hand side of the new Leisure Centre and through car parks to the rear until you reach the banks of the River Dane.

This area of the River Dane was the location of medieval salt workers. The town's brine pit was located adjacent to the River Dane and 'wich' or salt houses lined the street either side.

Follow the meander of the River Dane around on a paved footpath. Keep the railway arches on your left, cross the river via a footbridge and continue until you reach the road. Cross the road via the pelican crossing and turn left. The Weaver Hall Museum and Workhouse is 150 yards on the right.

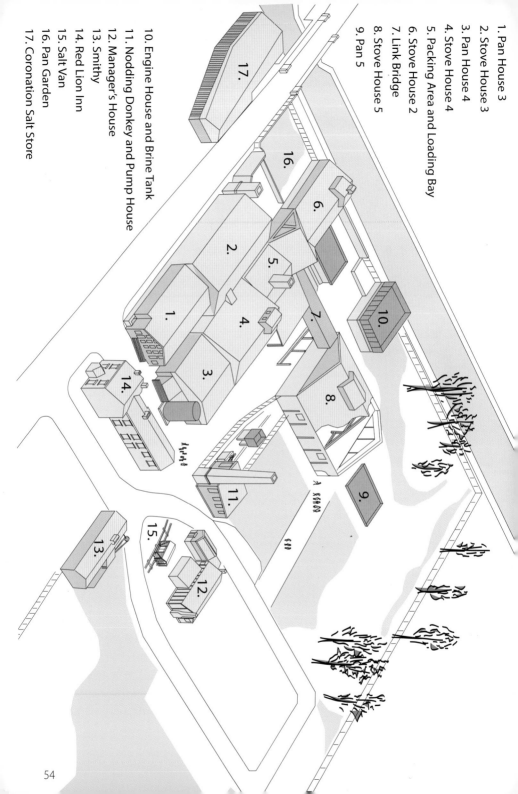

1. Pan House 3
2. Stove House 3
3. Pan House 4
4. Stove House 4
5. Packing Area and Loading Bay
6. Stove House 2
7. Link Bridge
8. Stove House 5
9. Pan 5
10. Engine House and Brine Tank
11. Nodding Donkey and Pump House
12. Manager's House
13. Smithy
14. Red Lion Inn
15. Salt Van
16. Pan Garden
17. Coronation Salt Store